THE
happiness
&
contentment
WORKBOOK

Written by SURYACITTA (THE HAPPY BUDDHA)
Illustrated by Ruth Allen

chartwell
books

Text © 2020 Suryacitta
Design and layout © 2020 Quarto Publishing plc

This edition published in 2021 by Chartwell Books,
an imprint of The Quarto Group
142 West 36th Street, 4th Floor
New York, NY 10018 USA
T (212) 779-4972 F (212) 779-6058
www.Quarto.com

Contains content originally published in the UK
and North America in 2020 by
Leaping Hare Press
An imprint of The Quarto Group
The Old Brewery, 6 Blundell Street
London N7 9BH, United Kingdom
T (0)20 7700 6700

10 9 8 7 6 5 4 3 2

Chartwell titles are also available at discount for retail, wholesale, promotional, and bulk purchase. For details, contact the Special Sales Manager by email at specialsales@quarto.com or by mail at The Quarto Group, Attn: Special Sales Manager, 100 Cummings Center Suite 265D, Beverly, MA 01915, USA.

ISBN: 978-0-7858-4065-7

Publisher: David Breuer
Editorial Director: Tom Kitch
Art Director: James Lawrence
Commissioning Editor: Monica Perdoni
Project Editor: Elizabeth Clinton
Design Manager: Anna Stevens
Designer: Wayne Blades
Cover Designer: Kate Sinclair
Publishing Assistant: Chloe Murphy

Printed in China

CONTENTS

Chapter 1:
Becoming Mushy   4

Chapter 2:
The Broken Vase   22

Chapter 3:
The Big Picture   34

Chapter 4:
Know Your Inner Critic   48

Chapter 5:
Grandmother Mind   62

Chapter 6:
Where Is Your Wildness?   76

Chapter 7:
It's Those Little People Again   90

Chapter 8:
Your True Home   98

Chapter 9:
The Forgotten Medicine   108

Chapter 10:
Are You Nexting?   126

My Happy Thoughts   144

Chapter One

BECOMING MUSHY

Imagine a large ice cube. At its center shines a beautiful, glittering jewel. The jewel represents our innate happiness and joy – but because it's encased in the ice cube, we don't have access to it.

What is the ice in this analogy? It is what we call our 'rigidly held beliefs', the thoughts and attitudes that keep the jewel frozen. Do we feel compelled to be a certain kind of person all the time? Do we identify ourselves entirely with our religion, our politics, our supposed personality traits? Of course we all have faiths and philosophies, but when we let them harden around us, we can become lost within them. Our life's work is to put that ice in the warmth of the sun, so it begins to melt, getting mushy and then draining away, gradually revealing the joy that has been there all the time.

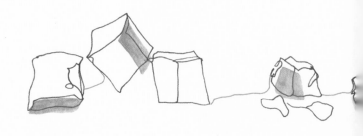

Now what does this mean for us? How do we melt
the ice of our unhappiness, our rigidly held, limiting beliefs?
Well, that is the work contained in this book.

It means being honest with ourselves. It means turning towards
our own upsets, rather than blaming the world. It means learning
to be grateful, rather than taking things and people for granted.
It means seeing that your demands on life are making you unhappy,
and if you can hold them lightly, contentment awaits you.

Melting the ice means not turning away from your own sadness,
but allowing it space to guide you to compassion and happiness.

BECOMING MUSHY

MELTING THE ICE

If happiness is already here, what are we doing to hold it back? This is really the million-dollar question.

We seem almost addicted to making ourselves unhappy. One of the ways we do this is a simple idea: that if life goes our way, we will feel contented. But does that work?

The truth is, we are often unaware of what we really believe, including beliefs that, all unknowingly, make us sad. With a little meditation and quiet time we can bring them into the light.

Sit quietly and feel the breath for a few minutes. Ask the questions (right) as you would drop a pebble into a pond, and see what bubbles up. Write down your responses.

What stops me from being happy?

What REALLY stops me from being happy?

What things could I do that make me happy?

What other things could I do that make me happy?

MY LIMITING BELIEFS

Beliefs are unexamined assumptions and views on life. Limiting beliefs are those which hold us back. Just by believing them, we stop acting and speaking in a way which feels natural to us.

One limiting belief may be that you are unworthy, or that you are useless. Another may be that you don't deserve to be successful. Perhaps you believe you are better and more important than others, that people won't like you if they really know you, or that you have to be nice all the time to be liked and accepted.

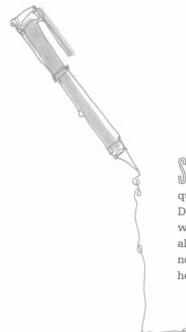

Sit quietly and feel yourself breathe for a few minutes. Then look at the questions opposite, and fill in the blanks. Don't think about your answers; just write what comes. It does not matter at all what arises, even if it appears to be nonsense: you are just clearing the way here for clarity.

My deepest limiting belief is . . .

I cling to this belief because I am . . .

The biggest belief that makes me unhappy is . . .

If I dropped this belief I would be/feel . . .

I deeply believe that I can . . .

I deeply believe that I cannot . . .

A LITTLE FORGIVENESS (PART ONE)

One of the ways we form the ice that separates us from our natural, happy state is to hold onto resentments. These may be what people have said or done to us, or what we have said and done ourselves. Many of us seem not very good at forgiving.

The trouble is, someone has to begin the forgiveness process, otherwise life turns into an endless cycle of reciprocal grudges and resentments. Somebody criticizes us, so we criticize them back. Somebody snubs us, so we snub them. We can hold onto things for days, weeks, months and even decades. When we hold on, we cannot be happy, because happiness is allowing life to flow freely, without interrupting it with resistance whenever we don't like something.

Sit quietly for a few minutes and feel yourself breathe. Now, take your attention to your heart center, the center of your chest that represents your spiritual heart. Bring to mind somebody who has hurt you, think about it for a few moments, and notice how it feels. Do you feel tense? Angry?

Now just drop the whole thing into the heart. Don't think about how to do this, just drop it into the heart. Now watch it dissolve very subtly. If you go into your head, come back to the heart.

After the meditation, you can write down the name of the person and what you forgave to reinforce your resolution.

I forgive . . .

for . . .

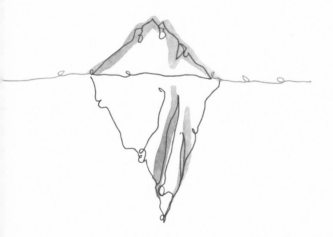

A LITTLE FORGIVENESS (PART ONE)

A LITTLE FORGIVENESS (PART TWO)

Next, it's time to forgive ourselves. It's one of the most important things to do at the end of each day: you can learn from mistakes, but it is best not to drag them into bed to keep you awake. Many of us suffer from what we call the chattering mood or mental proliferation: the tendency of the mind to dwell on things which bother us, and go over them again and again. This happens because we haven't healed the emotion, so the mind gets going trying to solve it. All the thinking in this case just creates more distress.

Sit quietly and feel your breath for a few minutes, then bring to mind something you said or did today that may have been unkind or thoughtless. Be honest here; we all do this. Notice how it makes you feel, then, after a few moments, again just drop it into the heart. If you find yourself in your head again, go back to the heart. The heart always forgives. Once you've finished the meditation, you can write down what you forgave yourself for. Do this every evening.

I forgive myself for . . .

A LITTLE FORGIVENESS (PART TWO)

FROM THINKING TO SENSING

As most of us know, we spend far too much time in our heads thinking about everything, and most of that thinking is absolutely useless. Research by Harvard University in the United States found that most people spend 46.9 percent of their waking hours thinking about something other than what they're doing, and this mind-wandering typically makes them unhappy.

I think this is a conservative figure, but it is still very revealing. Over-thinking not only creates the ice we mentioned earlier, but makes us anxious.

What we need to do is to move from a life of over-thinking to a life of sensing. Sensing is physical rather than intellectual, and when we are able to live in the body, we find our mind quietens.

Sit quietly and feel your breath for a few minutes. Now I want you to just feel your body, just sense it sitting here and experience all its different sensations. Notice at some point how you want to go into thinking, and when you notice that, just return to sensing the body. Choose a few different parts to focus on, such as the hands and the belly. Don't try to achieve anything at all. Just do it. When you've finished, fill in the blanks opposite.

I spend most of my day thinking about . . .

My biggest obsession is . . .

All this thinking leaves me . . .

I over-think because . . .

A life of sensing instead of over-thinking would leave me feeling. . .

FROM THINKING TO SENSING

BEFRIENDING DIFFICULT EMOTIONS

Many of us are uncomfortable with emotions: we don't quite know what to do about them. However, it is not the emotions we experience that are the problem: it is the ones we don't want to experience. For example, we may feel sad, but we don't want to, so we tend to repress it and it goes into the body and gets stuck there.

What we need to learn to do is experience our emotional life so that it all flows freely and easily. The emotions arise, and they pass through, and we don't interrupt the natural process.

We find this difficult because we want life to be predictable and orderly. Emotions, though, are messy and they can arrive at the most delicate of times and can be both uncomfortable and embarrassing.

Building on the previous exercise, sit quietly and feel your breath for a few minutes. When you feel ready, begin sensing into your body. Out of that sensing you may begin to feel something uncomfortable, maybe a tension, a heaviness or a tightness somewhere. It may be something more emotional, like a sadness or frustration. I want you to just feel whatever you find. What you feel, you heal. Just feel it for a few minutes, and don't try to do anything to it.

After that, on the drawing below locate where the feelings were felt. Use different colors for different feelings.

BEFRIENDING DIFFICULT EMOTIONS

LET'S MEET THE CONTROLLER

One of the reasons we don't want to experience certain emotions is because we all have what we can call an inner controller, a sub-personality whose purpose is to make sure we don't feel threatened. For some it will be sadness that feels like a threat; for others it may be anger, and for others it may be saying no. We each have a range of feelings that we become somewhat comfortable with, and anything outside of that range, this sub-personality can find threatening.

We all need a controller who looks out for us, but if it is over-developed, it can become problematic: it puts us permanently on guard against any emotion it considers intolerable. Let us meet the controller and listen to what they have to say.

Sit quietly and feel your breath for a few minutes. When you feel ready, I want you to take the pen in your dominant hand and ask the controller a question.

To respond, you are going to take the pen in your non-dominant hand and write a response. Don't think about this; just write. It may be illegible, but that doesn't matter.

Here are some questions to help you get going:

* Hello controller, how are you today?
* Are you around much in my life?
* What is your purpose in my life?
* What scares you?
* If you were standing in front of me what would you look like?
* What do you need from me?

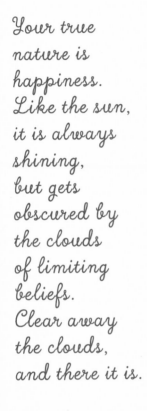

*Your true
nature is
happiness.
Like the sun,
it is always
shining,
but gets
obscured by
the clouds
of limiting
beliefs.
Clear away
the clouds,
and there it is.*

IDENTIFYING MASKS

We all wear masks, and we all hide behind them. The very word 'person' derives from the Latin word *persona*, which means an actor's mask. We wear different masks in different situations: a different mask at home, for instance, from the ones we use at work or when playing a sport.

One of our greatest fears is showing our true selves, because we are encouraged by our culture to be 'somebody', to be better, greater, more successful and so on. As a consequence, we lose touch with who we

1 Take off the mask of your name and put it to one side.

2 Take off the mask of your age.

3 Take off the mask of your profession, even if you don't have one; that too is a mask.

4 Take off the mask or the label of your political beliefs, even if you are not interested in politics, as that too is a mask.

really are and suffer for that. We hear a lot of advice like, 'Just be yourself,' but we find it very difficult to follow. The problem is that we get so used to our masks that we lose touch with our natural state, our authentic way of being. All the while we're hiding, we long just to be ourselves, to be authentically who we are without apology.

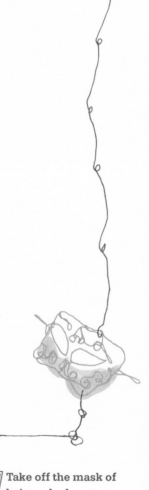

REMOVING YOUR MASKS

Sit quietly and feel your breath for a few minutes. Now I am going to ask you to enter your imagination and take off a few masks. Allow yourself to just feel and see what is behind each of them. Just see what it is like to be free of them, if only for a few minutes. Allow 30 seconds or so between each request.

5 Take of the mask of your spiritual self; if you are not spiritual take that one off too.

6 Take off the mask of being a good person.

7 Take off the mask of being a bad person.

Chapter Two

THE BROKEN VASE

There was once a Buddhist Zen master called Haku, who was 90 years of age. He had a friend called Basho, the same age as himself. They were both abbots of monasteries in neighbouring villages; the two had been ordained together many years ago and were great friends. Haku wanted to visit Basho, so he let the monks and nuns know and that he hoped to be back in seven days. He put one of the nuns in charge in his absence.

They had a great time reminiscing and drinking their *sake*. Seven days passed, and it was time for Haku return to his monastery. They hugged each other, and he set out.

Just before he returned, his lovely dedicated cleaning lady decided to clean his room for him. He was always so kind to her and her family. It was the least she could do to show her gratitude.

She dusted the shelves, washed the surfaces, and then she saw his favorite ceramic vase. He cherished this vase and took great care of it, as it was a gift at his ordination from his master. She picked up the vase, preparing to dust it, when it slipped from her fingers and shattered into a hundred pieces. At that moment the door handle began to move – bear in mind here that although Zen masters can be very compassionate, they can also be very stern when needed – and the door slowly creaked open.

She looked over to him, alarmed.

He walked over to her, looked her in the eye, and said, 'Don't you worry, my dear. I got that vase for pleasure, not for pain.'

He sat her down, made her a cup of tea and asked her how her family was.

This is one of my favorite stories and contains profound wisdom when we reflect upon it.

THE BROKEN VASE

WHY DID THE ZEN MASTER RESPOND LIKE THAT?

The vase was dropped and broken. However, the Zen master was not surprised, because it is the destiny of everything to come to an end. Knowing this truth deeply was one of the reasons why he cherished the vase in the first place. Because it was fragile, he needed to take care of it, but he also didn't expect it to last for ever.

Consider: do we cherish a plastic vase as much as a china one? Probably not: it can be dropped and it needs less tender treatment – so we feel less tenderness towards it.

Our lives and our friendships are also fragile, more like the ceramic vase than the plastic. One day they too will come to an end; even if we remain friends with someone till death, that last moment will eventually come. So, likewise, we need to cherish and take care of ourselves and our friendships.

Write here the names of friends you cherish.

 1

 2

 3

 4

 5

 6

WHY DID THE ZEN MASTER RESPOND LIKE THAT?

BEGINNINGS

It's easy to underestimate the value of the people and things in our lives, and this includes underestimating ourselves.

Why do we do this? One reason is that there's a truth that scares us: life is wonderful and fragile, and wonderful because it's fragile. Opening to the impermanence opens us up to the beauty. The ending could not exist without the beginning, and while it lasts, it is lovely.

Sit quietly and feel your breath for a few minutes.

1 **Notice how each breath has a beginning and an end.**

2 **Every moment in your life, there is a beginning and an ending. Allow yourself to feel your responses to this truth.**

3 **Look back on your life, and allow beginnings to come to mind.**

4 Think of someone that you used to know. Don't focus on the ending; just think of them as you knew them.

5 Feel the pleasure or the pain of this. A good life is a mixture of both.

Do this with two or three people. Write your responses in the space above after the exercise.

ENDINGS

Most of us much prefer beginnings to endings. Endings remind us of the final ending of our own lives, which we'd rather put out of mind. However, if we are to be happy we have to begin to face the facts of life; it's clinging to beliefs we know to be untrue that causes the real suffering.

Sit quietly and feel your breath for a few minutes.

1 Bring to mind the people from the previous exercise, and focus on the ending of your relationship with them.

2 They entered your life, perfumed it, and they have gone again. Notice the pleasant or the unpleasant feelings.

3 If a person who came to mind is still in your life, open up to the idea of them leaving in one way or another. Welcome all feelings and emotions here. Beginnings and endings are a fact of life.

4 Write down your responses in the space above after the exercise.

When
you feel the
fragility of life,
you feel the
wonder of life.

BEFRIENDING YOUR JEALOUS SELF

Have you ever picked up what has looked like a perfect red apple, only to see that a worm has burrowed inside and eaten half of it, and what is left is rotten?

For me, this is symbolic of jealousy. Jealousy eats away at our contentment. It can leave us feeling hollow, focused on what we don't have and what other people do, or on what we might lose. With such thoughts in our mind, it's no wonder that we feel bad.

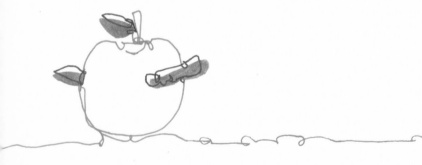

1 **Find two chairs and place them a few feet apart.**

2 **Find something to represent the jealous part of you. It may just be a sheet of paper with 'Jealousy' written on it or an object of some sort. Don't over-think this, just do it.**

3 **Sit quietly and feel your breath for a few minutes.**

How are you right now?

How old are you?

What do you need from me to be OK?

What do you really need from me to be OK?

4 **Look over to your jealous self and say, 'Hello, jealous part.' Then ask the questions on the right. Take your time and allow yourself to feel any responses that arise and write them down.**

BEFRIENDING YOUR JEALOUS SELF

BOUNDARIES

One of the things I have noticed over many years working with students is just how important personal boundaries are, and just how many of us struggle with having them. I once heard somebody say that you cannot be compassionate if you don't have boundaries, and I thought this was a very interesting point.

Firstly, if you are excluded from your own compassion then it is not compassion. You have to extend it to yourself as well. Otherwise it's just self-sacrifice.

Secondly, if you don't have boundaries – that is, the ability to say no or that enough is enough – then your compassion is likely to be a form of approval-seeking. It may look like niceness from the outside, but there will be the attitude of wanting something back, such as needing to be liked.

Surprisingly, not having boundaries limits our gratitude, because we feel taken advantage of. Gratitude and resentment cannot live together.

Sit quietly and feel your breath for a few minutes. When you feel ready, ask yourself these questions (right) and allow yourself to feel the answer in your body.

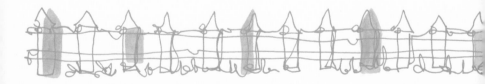

What stops me from having stronger personal boundaries?

_____

How would my life be if I had stronger boundaries?

What part of me am I trying to protect by not having boundaries?

Boundaries I will do my best to set

BOUNDARIES

Chapter Three

THE BIG PICTURE

Each morning when you wake up, it is as if you reach for a balloon. You huff and puff, trying to inflate it – and then a few minutes after getting out of bed, life comes along and bursts the thing. You instantly reach for another balloon, and blow that one up too. Again, life comes along and bursts it. It's an exhausting cycle, and it's how we spend our days.

Into these balloons we blow our expectations and demands for the day ahead, the week ahead, and so on. Some of these demands are about ourselves, other people, or life in general.

Another way of looking at this is that we all have a picture of how we believe life should be. It is not that having a picture is wrong;

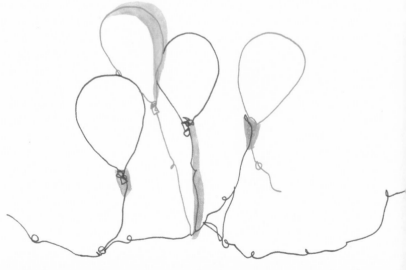

we cannot live without one, but it causes problems when we cling
to that picture and encounter something that doesn't fit into it
and get upset about that.

This is a very crucial point. Instead of learning about our picture
here, we tend to go into blaming. We may blame others for making
us feel a certain way, or we blame ourselves for not being perfect.
Either way, we don't learn anything. We could instead take this
moment to pause and ask ourselves: what is my picture?

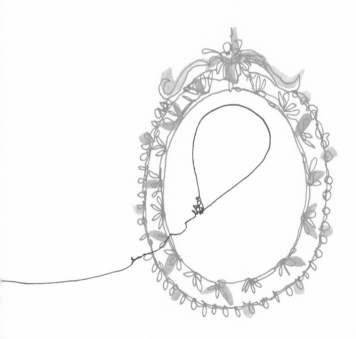

WHAT IS MY PICTURE?

The problem is not what our picture contains, but how tightly we hold onto that picture. We may think that we'll find happiness if we can make a life that reflects the picture, but the truth is that it's the picture that's making us unhappy: life is life and won't always comply, and being hypervigilant for such moments is only going to make us tense. Happiness is welcoming the whole of life, whether it matches our picture-perfect image or not.

Sit quietly and follow your breath for a few minutes. Then, when you feel ready, ask yourself these questions slowly and spaciously.

What is my picture of happiness today?

How does my life need to be for me to be happy today?

If this picture is not met, will I be unhappy?

Can I allow myself to be happy even if my picture is not met?

Draw or write your imperfect picture of life and get comfortable with it. If you choose to draw, it doesn't matter whether it's 'good' or not: your drawings, too, are allowed to be imperfect!

MORNING MEDITATION

When you wake in the morning, it is an opportunity to tune into yourself. Sleep leaves us with many feelings, some from our dream life and some about the day ahead.

Many people wake in the morning with feelings of dread. At this point, we may begin catastrophizing – or we can do something different. We can turn towards the body and see if anything wants our attention.

Have you ever noticed that you would rather be right than happy? How would you be if you dropped the demand to be right?

With eyes open or closed, focus on your body and see what feelings want your attention. Just feel them. Is there a sense of sadness, is there a feeling of fear, or do you feel rested? Attend for five or ten minutes. Write down what you noticed in order to clear your head for the day.

MORNING MEDITATION

WORKING WITH UPSETS

When we feel upset that the world doesn't match our mental picture, that can be a good time to learn about the demands we make of life. We are often angry because our desires have been thwarted in some way, and looking for someone to blame, but there may also be hurt or sadness.

What we need to do first is soothe ourselves. Of course, if somebody has been nasty or unkind in some way we may need to say something to them, but this is often best done once we have cleared away the red mist of anger.

Sit quietly for a few minutes then fill in the blanks opposite:

I get upset when . . .

. . . upsets me at work because . . .

I get angry at . . .

because . . .

I am scared to speak up because . . .

To stop getting so upset I wish I could . . .

When I get upset I feel it in my . . .

One thing that would help me to get less upset would be . . .

WORKING WITH UPSETS

SHOW YOUR APPRECIATION

How often have you had the urge to say something appreciative to somebody, but then talked yourself out of it, for fear of looking foolish or silly? What would happen if we just spoke aloud the kind thoughts that came into our minds?

We can see doing this as a kind of re-wiring of the brain. Many of us tend to criticize others or say uncharitable things, but with a little willingness, we can change this.

Choose a day, perhaps today if it's early in the morning, or tomorrow. Make the intention (not a serious solemn vow) of saying whatever appreciative comments come to mind. If you struggle with this, pick a person you know and reflect on them for five minutes. Write down what you admire about them and, when the time is right, say it.

I admire . . .

SHOW YOUR APPRECIATION

DIFFICULT SITUATIONS

We all face difficult situations, and we all have strategies to avoid them. These strategies can develop early in childhood, and can become automatic reactions. For example, one person may be agreeable to everybody to avoid conflict; another may close down emotionally when things get tough; one person may go for all-out attack when they feel threatened, while another might turn everything into a joke.

We all have these strategies, and they can make us feel inauthentic. A way of freeing ourselves from the grasp is to notice without judgment when they are activated.

Choose a day and make the intention of simply noticing ways you are inauthentic. Perhaps you agree when really you don't, or fudge the answer to a question rather than tell the truth. At the end of the day, write down the responses you gave and the responses you really wanted to give.

What I said . . .

What I really think . . .

DIFFICULT SITUATIONS

PRESENCE OF MIND

Most of us don't like to feel judged. When we are criticized, it can really rock our boat, and we don't like to feel vulnerable. As the philosopher Elbert Hubbard put it, though, 'To escape criticism: Do nothing, say nothing, be nothing' – which is a life hardly worth living. It's much better to be ourselves, and to be able to meet criticism when it comes our way.

Of course, there is constructive criticism, which we need to be able to take and learn from. However, we often don't have the presence of mind to know the difference between that and an unfair attack, so it's worth developing your skills there.

Next time you are being criticized or judged, instead of striking back and maybe regretting it later, learn to feel your breath. The desire to lash out lasts for only a second or two, like a wave on the shore. Let it rise, then let it dissolve away. Then you can respond to the person with greater wisdom.

Think back to some scenarios where you instantly went on the attack. Write down everything about the situation – who was there, who you attacked, what they had done to upset you. Then rewrite the scenario with you taking a pause to notice your breath, and think what you could have said instead with presence of mind.

What happened . . .

What could have happened . . .

PRESENCE OF MIND

Chapter Four

KNOW YOUR INNER CRITIC

There have been times in my life when the inner critic has been so strong it has paralyzed me. It would dictate to me what I could and couldn't say, what I could and could not wear. If I was in company and I wanted to tell a story or give an opinion, it would show its angry little head, saying things like, 'People will think you are stupid; you will show yourself up, you idiot.'

It sat like a tyrant on my shoulder making sure I did exactly as I was told. It would even be there in my meditation practice, telling me I wasn't trying hard enough. Then, when I tried harder, it would criticize me for trying too hard.

In my work I see the effects of people's inner critic. The critic can be so strong it makes people miserable, and even scared – not only of other people, but themselves. For some people it can drive them to seek success, but of course, the success is never enough, so they often burn themselves out.

Many of us just want the inner critic to disappear. But wishing it would go away doesn't work. Going to war on it doesn't work either. Some people criticize themselves for being self-critical; I wonder who is doing that criticism?

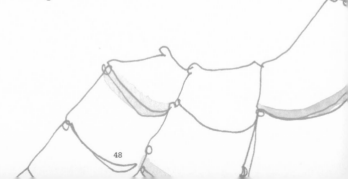

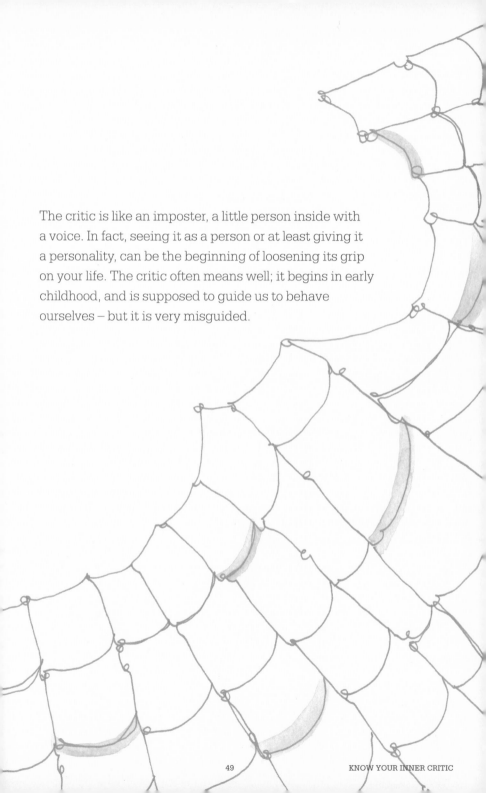

The critic is like an imposter, a little person inside with a voice. In fact, seeing it as a person or at least giving it a personality, can be the beginning of loosening its grip on your life. The critic often means well; it begins in early childhood, and is supposed to guide us to behave ourselves – but it is very misguided.

HELLO THERE, INNER CRITIC

We can adopt many strategies for dealing with the inner critic. You may have your own, but if you are reading this, then they may not have been very successful.

I have met some people who will debate with the critic, offering a different view to its own. Other ways are learning to let go of those thoughts through meditation, and this is one of the ways I recommend. This way, we can befriend it, listen to it and learn not to take its opinions personally.

Questions you might ask

* How long have you been around in my life?
* Would you like me to call you by a specific name?
* What is your purpose in my life?
* What is your ultimate purpose in my life?
* What scares you?

1 Sit quietly for a few minutes and feel your breath.

2 Pick up your pen and write: 'Hello there, inner critic, how are you today?' in the space above right.

3 Take your pen in your non-dominant hand and reply. Don't think about your response; just write it. The writing may look like a child's writing, but that does not matter.

4 Ask it some other questions, keeping them simple and direct. Treat it like a conversation.

5 If your critic tells you to shut up, stay with the exercise. You are building a relationship with it.

You can start with the questions on the far left, but mainly you are having a conversation, so treat it like one and go where it leads.

LISTEN TO YOUR INNER CRITIC

The inner critic will make itself known in situations where you feel uncomfortable or insecure; insecurity is often what creates the inner critic in the first place.

What we need is awareness and knowledge of its voice, rather than trying to banish it or pretend it isn't there. For some people the voice of the critic resembles a voice from the past, perhaps a mother, or a father, an aunt, or a teacher, or it may be a combination of these people in our earlier lives. It is worth knowing, however, that whoever it sounds like, the inner critic is trying to help you. It is just doing a job, and that job is all it knows.

Thoughts are like hooks, learn the beautiful and simple art of unhooking from negative thoughts (page 92) and return to your breath.

Sit quietly for a few minutes and feel your breath. When you are ready, begin to communicate with the inner critic. Ask some or all of the example questions, and see what arises.

Questions you might ask

* What makes you happy?
* What emotion is running you?
* What situations are you most present in?
* What are your favorite phrases you say to me?
* How can I help you?
* What do you need from me?
* Where do you live in my body?
* How old are you?
* If you were standing in front of me, what would you look like?

LISTEN TO YOUR INNER CRITIC

HAPPY BIRTHDAY

Thoughts in themselves are not a problem;
it is when we believe them and take them
personally that they cause the trouble. They
often arise without our willing them to, but
we still tend to take them as a reflection of
who we are.

When we get locked into a story, particularly
a negative one, we can lose our lightness and
joy. What we need to do is to stop taking our
thoughts to heart; the sorrow they cause is
fuelled by belief.

Sit quietly for a few minutes and
feel your breath. Think of a
critical thought; make it a real one,
something you say to yourself in your
daily life. Notice how it makes you
feel: not very pleasant, I assume.
Think it to yourself for twenty
seconds.

Now sing that same thought
back to yourself to the tune of
'Happy Birthday'. Notice the
difference and write it down.

When singing the negative thought I noticed . . .

HAPPY BIRTHDAY

SHOULD-ISM

When I started practicing meditation and then Buddhism many years ago, I was very earnest and keen in my practice. When I joined the Buddhist community, there were lots of other young men as keen as myself. At the time I always did the 'right' thing, always did what I thought I should do, so I was seen as a good Buddhist.

I remember listening to my teacher speaking once and he said that a lot of people new to Buddhism do not practice Buddhism, but instead practice should-ism. This struck me as so true: I was listening to the voice which always started with 'I should'.

I see many people nowadays who are listening to the 'I should' voice, which can leave them feeling frustrated and quite often exhausted. They feel that they should always be doing something, and that something is often for somebody else. Instead of just obeying the 'I should' voice, learn to let it go and feel the emotion behind it. Over time this voice and the emotion will weaken.

Sit quietly for a few minutes and feel your breath. Ask yourself the following questions and wait for each response. Write it down when it arrives.

I spend most of my day thinking about . . .

All this thinking leaves me . . .

I over-think because . . .

A life of sensing instead of over-thinking would leave me feeling . . .

THE ASSERTIVE SELF

From childhood on, we long for acceptance and, as a result, we may suppress some of our natural assertive instincts in a bid to please others. Of course, it's not wrong to be considerate, but if we end up thinking time and again, 'Why didn't I say that?' or 'If only I'd done this,' we have over-corrected, and can end up feeling depressed, anxious and full of blame.

It's time to get back in touch with your assertive self, and the first step is to recognize its absence.

Sit quietly for a few minutes and feel your breath. When you feel ready, just read slowly the phrases opposite and notice how you feel when reading each one. Note down your feelings.

 Expressing your own feelings and opinions

 Saying no without feeling guilty

 Expressing your anger

 Stating what you want

 Feeling resentful

 Always pleasing others

 Nodding along when really you don't agree

As we weaken the grip of the inner critic, we also strengthen the one voice I believe is absolutely essential to living a good life free from resentment and fear: the assertive voice. Or the voice that can say yes, and no, and mean it.

Sit quietly for a few minutes and feel your breath. Read through each question carefully and write your responses with your non-dominant hand. Don't think too hard, just write something.

 Hello there, assertive voice, how are you today?

 Are you around much in my life?

 Would you like to be around more in my life?

 What difference would you make to my life?

THE ASSERTIVE SELF

Chapter Five

GRANDMOTHER MIND

When I was a young boy, my mom would take me to my grandmother, who would care for me whilst my mom went out to work. I would see her door and I would run, open it and dash in. My grandmother would always be sitting in her favorite chair, reading her newspaper, but she would see me, drop the paper and would say something like, 'Come here and give me a big kiss now.' She would open her arms and cuddle me and kiss me all over. I loved this, of course, as I felt very special. My mom would sometimes say to her something like, 'He hasn't cleaned his room today,' or 'He's been naughty this morning'. My grandmother would reply, 'I don't care; leave him here with me and you go to work. Now give me another kiss,' she would say to me.

My grandmother welcomed everything about me, even the 'naughty' parts of me.

We all need to cultivate what I call the grandmother mind; a mind or an attitude of complete acceptance about who we are. So often we try to banish parts of ourselves which we feel are unacceptable. We may feel shame about certain parts of our body, or something we have done; we may turn away from painful feelings that we find hard to cope with. But the grandmother mind opens our heart to our own sadness, our own grief and, of course, to our own feelings of joy and wonder.

It may be that for you, that warm, nurturing figure was someone else. 'Grandmother mind' is what I'll be using here, in tribute to someone I deeply loved, but if another name for that mental state suits you better, choose whatever works for you. If there was no one who made you feel that accepted, you'll need to cultivate it within yourself as an archetype of the love you need and deserve.

GRANDMOTHER HEART

I write here of grandmother mind, but really it is actually grandmother heart. The head may be full of self-doubts or criticism, but the heart is a big, open, welcoming space and never says no to anything.

When we live and trust in the heart, our mind is quiet. Our mind can chatter away, trying to protect us, but when we live in the heart, it doesn't need to: we are relaxed and at ease. To place our trust in the heart is one of the greatest blessings we can know.

Next time you are facing a difficult situation, go into your heart. For example, you may have to go to a meeting or an interview that makes you feel nervous. What you will find is that you begin to over-think, making yourself more nervous. Instead, drop your attention onto your heart and walk into that meeting in touch with your own courage.

Sit quietly for a few minutes and feel your breath, then ask yourself these questions, slowly, giving yourself space to really hear them.

How would my life be if I trusted in my heart?

What prevents me from trusting in my heart?

Ask your heart if there is anything else it would like to reveal to you.

YOUR INNER CHILD

We all have an inner child. This being is very sensitive to the world, particularly to criticism and rejection: the child holds our vulnerability.

This can make it an uncomfortable psychic space for us: many of us prefer to hide our vulnerabilities rather than acknowledge them. The truth is, though, that they are beautiful: they are what allow us to be open and connect with others.

The word itself comes from the Latin for wound: *vulnus*. When we are open, we can be hurt – but it is also the only way we can be filled with wonder. We may want to shut down and stay safe, but that shuts out the beauty as well. Our road to happiness opens very gradually, and we cannot have the joy without the hurt: together they are life itself.

In this exercise, I want to encourage you to stay open to the inner child's other quality as well: its playfulness. The inner child holds a lot of energy, and if we listen to their voice and feel their presence, it can help bring them alive in our daily lives.

Sit quietly for a few minutes and feel your breath. When you feel ready, pick up a pen in your dominant hand and write, 'Hello inner child, how are you today?'

Then take the pen in your non-dominant hand and respond. Continue with your non-dominant hand and answer the following questions.

Hello . . .

Are you around much in my life?

What would you like me to call you?

What is your purpose in my life?

Tell me what things you like doing.

 What do you want from me?

 What do you need from me?

 What makes you sad?

What makes you angry?

 What makes you happy?

 How do you like to play?

 What would you like to do today?

YOUR INNER CHILD

BEFRIENDING SADNESS

I want to do a little more work around sadness. It's an interesting emotion: I meet a lot of people who have what can be called unacknowledged sadness. We don't want it, so we try to banish it. We can feel like there is something wrong with our life if we feel sad, but really, it's just the opposite: it is natural to feel sad at times. It just means you are alive and sensitive to the world.

Sorrow is the seed that blossoms into compassion. If I can allow myself to feel sad and to know what the experience is like, then I have the capacity to empathize and to feel compassion for the pain you feel too. In this way, that which hurts us can also connect us.

1 Sit and feel your breath for a few minutes.

2 For a few minutes, bring to mind a happy time with a friend or a loved one. Notice how it feels in your body. Does it feel light, expansive, open? Really pay attention.

3 Next, bring to mind a sad time; it doesn't have to be a really tragic event for this purpose. Now notice how that makes your body feel and what thoughts arise.

4 Now ask yourself: what is so bad about this feeling of sadness? Find out in your experience, not your thoughts, what is so bad about it.

5 Write down any responses.

BEFRIENDING SADNESS

CULTIVATING YOUR GRANDMOTHER MIND

We all have parts of ourselves we are not at ease with, or that we actively want to keep hidden away. It may be the shy part of us, or it may be the confident part. People ask me why somebody would want to keep their confident part hidden; the answer is that at some point it has been mistaken for being arrogant. Our culture values humility, and if our confidence isn't accepted when we are young, it generally goes into the shadows.

We can, however, begin to develop a more healthy relationship with these parts of ourselves, using meditation to allow them a kind of compassionate space where they are welcomed and can begin to blossom again.

Read through these instructions first, then do the meditations. Don't rush through them. You can do them over a number of days.

First, just reflect on and write down six traits about yourself with which you are uncomfortable. For example, if you don't like your shyness, write that down. If you don't like a part of your body, write that down too. It may even be that you don't like your inner critic; write that down.

1 Sit quietly for a few minutes, and begin to connect with your heart center. If you are unsure where this is, then bring your attention to the middle of your chest: this is your emotional and spiritual heart.

2 Choose the first item on your list, and invite it into your heart space. You can just sense this part of you, or else picture it in your mind's eye. Say hello to it, and let it be. Just feel it; that is all you need to do. Remember, grandmother mind welcomes everything.

3 After three to four minutes, invite into the heart space the next item on your list. Allow the two traits to sit together in your space of awareness. Can you just let them be there? If you feel resistant and you want to recoil that is OK: just feel that.

4 Keep going in this way until you've experienced every quality you listed. After a few minutes, say thank you, and bring the practice to an end.

CULTIVATING YOUR GRANDMOTHER MIND

ALLOWING, NOT IDENTIFYING

Life is made up of both pleasant and
unpleasant experiences. Realistically, we
can't have one without the other: the only
way to avoid pain would be to shut ourselves
down emotionally, and if we do that, we
banish joy as well. Experiencing sadness is
an essential part of life. Sorrow does not mean
there is something wrong with you or your
life; on the contrary it means you are an
emotionally healthy human being

1 Sit quietly for a few minutes and follow your breath.

2 Now become aware of your heart space. Spend a minute or so just tuning in.

3 I want you to bring to mind something unpleasant that has happened to you. It may be something you did, or something somebody said or did to you. Just hold it in your heart space. Don't push it away. Do this for a couple of minutes.

4 Then bring to mind something pleasant that has happened. Again, just hold this in awareness.

5 Finally, I want you to hold both the pleasant and the unpleasant in your heart space. Focus on one, then the other. Notice how you may prefer the pleasant. That is OK. But just hold them there equally as best you can.

This is a metaphor for life: there is pleasantness and unpleasantness and we must face them both.

Write down your experience.

Chapter Six

WHERE IS YOUR WILDNESS?

In my work with people, for over twenty-five years now, there is one thing that stands out when people are unhappy and struggling with their lives: they have lost touch with their wildness. Their wild energy was around when they were children, and maybe made it into adulthood, but at some point, most of us discard it like an old worn-out piece of clothing.

We become overly responsible and lose touch with this wonderful part of ourselves. As adults with obligations, we think there is no place for the wild in our lives. It may be also that there doesn't seem to be enough time to indulge these energies.

Many people come to me claiming that they don't feel alive any more. If they don't say that, I can tell by the look on their face that they are yearning to reclaim their wild selves. However, we tend to be wary of wildness, some people align it with being irresponsible. The truth is, the two have nothing to do with each other.

You wild energy is your life energy. It connects to nature, to people, and to yourself. It is joy and happiness manifesting right there in your body. We need to learn to feel it again; we need to learn to feel everything again, to get out of our heads and start living.

One of the reasons we are scared of this energy is that we believe it will have us doing bungee jumping, or leaving our family and climbing Everest without a woolly hat; that people will think us silly or that we have 'lost the plot'. Nothing could be further from the truth. I am not going to tell you what your wild energy would like to do; you are just going to listen to it yourself.

WHERE IS YOUR WILDNESS?

WELCOME BACK, WILD SELF

1 Sit quietly and listen to any sounds you can hear right now.

2 When you feel ready, pick up a pen in your dominant hand and write on the page opposite, 'Hello, wild self; how are you today?'

Questions you might ask

* Are you around much in my life?
* Would you like to be around more in my life?
* What would you bring to my life if you were around more?
* How old are you?
* What things do you like doing?
* What things would you like me to do?
* Do you like having time with me like this?
* Where do you live in my body?
* How often should I visit you?
* Is there anything else you would like to say to me?

3 Then take the pen in your non-dominant hand, and just reply. Don't think about this; just write a line or two.

4 Enter into a dialogue, asking some other questions. Take your time and feel the energy of the inner wild self in your body.

LISTEN TO YOUR INNER REBEL

Most people, if you asked them, would want to feel more alive. The trouble is, we have many responsibilities that work against this.

Our sensible side isn't the whole of us, though: there are many more inner selves connected to the wild self, and they hold a lot of our life force. Many of us keep a lid on them, as we are scared of what it might mean if we let them out. However, all these parts want is to be listened to and acknowledged. They don't want to take over; they just want to be a part of the family.

A sub-personality associated with the wild self is the rebel. If you are eager to fit in then your rebel may be banished. In this exercise we are going to dialogue with your inner rebel.

Sit quietly for a few minutes and feel your breath. When you feel ready take the pen in your non-dominant hand and answer the questions opposite.

Hello inner rebel, how are you today?

Are you around much in my life?

Would you like to be around more?

What would you bring to my life if you were around more?

Where do you live in my body?

How old are you?

Now that I am listening, what do you want to say to me?

Anything else?

GREETINGS, PEOPLE PLEASER

One of the inner selves that plays a large part in our lives is the people pleaser. A strong people pleaser can keep out the more vital and alive selves such as the wild self and the rebel. Of course, wanting to make people happy is not a bad thing in itself; it's only a problem when it gets out of balance, so that we smile, talk nicely, and make sure everybody is OK, except ourselves.

The people pleaser is terrified of being disliked and disapproved of. Running around trying to avoid this when really we need to rest and attend to our own needs can be exhausting.

Sit quietly for a few minutes and feel your breath. When you feel ready, take the pen in your non-dominant hand and answer the following questions:

Hello people pleaser, how are you today?

Are you around much in my life?

How old are you?

How long have you been around in my life?

What is your purpose in my life?

What situations are you present in?

What emotion is running you?

What scares you?

What do you need from me to be OK?

HELLO, DEAR PERFECTIONIST

Another inner self worth exploring is the perfectionist, which can take up much of our energy and spontaneity. However, as in most of the other inner selves, it is not all bad: there are times when we need to do things to the best of our ability. High standards have their place: if you're a surgeon, you want to get things right – but don't carry the perfectionist with you when go home to your partner or children.

In this exercise we are going to liaise with the perfectionist and see what makes it tick.

Sit quietly for a few minutes and feel your breath. When you feel ready, take the pen in your non-dominant hand and answer the questions opposite.

 Hello perfectionist, how are you today?

 Are you around much in my life?

 What is your purpose?

 In which areas of my are you around most?

 What scares you the most?

 When you are around how do you make me feel?

HELLO THERE,
SPONTANEOUS SELF

Many of us assume that we can tell ourselves
what to do, and then do it; how to feel, and
then feel it; what to think, and then think it.
We may not fully believe this, but if you are
honest, you probably wish it were the case.
However, life is messy: there are twists and
turns, and our inability to stop them
happening makes us anxious. To help us
here, we need to reconnect with the wild-self
energy and its relative, the spontaneous self.

The spontaneous self doesn't have to be forever
thinking and pondering on things; it can just
do. It doesn't need a reason, it just acts, living
in the moment and seeing life afresh.

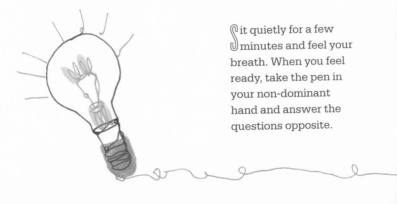

Sit quietly for a few
minutes and feel your
breath. When you feel
ready, take the pen in
your non-dominant
hand and answer the
questions opposite.

 Hello spontaneous self, how are you today?

 Are you around much in my life?

 Would you like to be around more?

 How old are you?

What would you bring to my life if you were around more?

HELLO, COURAGEOUS SELF

Maya Angelou once said, 'One isn't
necessarily born with courage, but one
is born with potential. Without courage,
we cannot practice any other virtue with
consistency. We can't be kind, true, merciful,
generous or honest.'

Our courageous self allows us to live the life
we want to live and to meet its challenges.
To be in touch with our courage, we need to
get out of our head and into the heart.

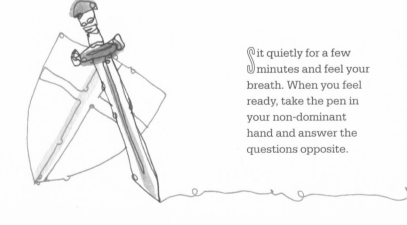

Sit quietly for a few
minutes and feel your
breath. When you feel
ready, take the pen in
your non-dominant
hand and answer the
questions opposite.

 Hello courageous self, how are you today?

 Are you around much in my life?

 How would you change my life if you were around more?

 Where do you live in my body?

 How can you be around more in my life?

Chapter Seven

IT'S THOSE LITTLE PEOPLE AGAIN

In Jonathan Swift's novel, *Gulliver's Travels*, the narrator is shipwrecked and washes up on the shores of Lilliput, a nation inhabited by people no more than six inches (15 cm) tall. Gulliver, to them, is a giant, and more than a match for any attack they might make on him, but the Lilliputians still manage to tie him down. How do they manage it? Simple: they wait until he falls asleep. Gulliver can't be alert all the time, so he gets caught, and has to struggle to extricate himself – and even though he can break the ropes, he still finds himself a subject of the Lilliputians.

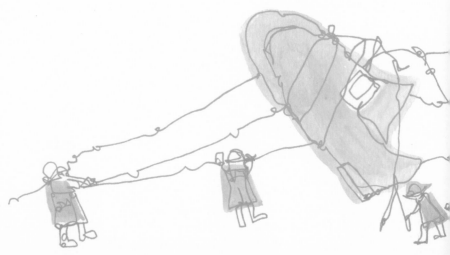

They draw him into ridiculous situations such as fighting a war over whether one should crack a boiled egg at the big end or the little. Why? He lets himself get talked into it. They regard themselves as high and mighty, and he takes them at their own estimation.

Our thoughts can be this way too; negative thoughts in particular, but fantasies and distractions as well. The problem isn't the thoughts themselves; the Lilliputians weren't especially evil. The problem is when we get entangled in them and let them rule us – and this happens when we take them too seriously. Thinking is a wonderful tool, but we need to learn to use it, rather than letting it run our whole lives.

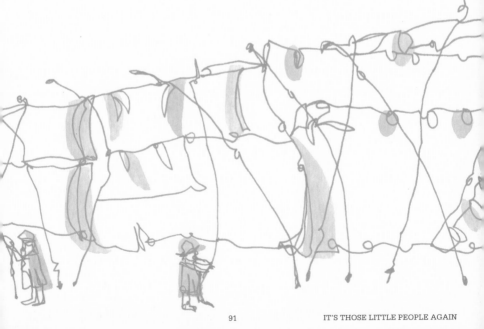

IT'S THOSE LITTLE PEOPLE AGAIN

THE ART OF UNHOOKING FROM THOUGHTS

Most of us know how one goes fishing. The fisher puts the worms on the hook, the fish comes along, and at some point, it bites the bait. The hook gets caught in the roof of its mouth; the more the fish struggles, the deeper the hook goes. The fisher then reels the fish out of its natural environment; it now cannot breathe, and begins to panic.

Our thoughts are like those hooks: they come along and we 'bite' and they take us out of our natural environment – the present moment – and we too can begin to panic. Try this exercise to help you unhook and return yourself to safety.

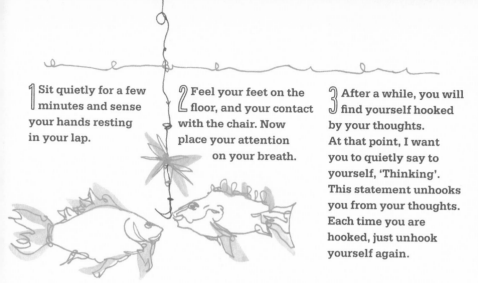

1 Sit quietly for a few minutes and sense your hands resting in your lap.

2 Feel your feet on the floor, and your contact with the chair. Now place your attention on your breath.

3 After a while, you will find yourself hooked by your thoughts. At that point, I want you to quietly say to yourself, 'Thinking'. This statement unhooks you from your thoughts. Each time you are hooked, just unhook yourself again.

Write down your experience.

THE GIFT OF NOW

There are two realities in life: the reality of being here now, in your five senses, and the unreality of your storytelling mind. I don't mean to say that the thoughts are unreal themselves, but the stories they tell often are. To be happy and content, we need to spend more time in the here and now with life as it is, instead of in the often troubling world of our thoughts.

What we need to see here is that thoughts can be very useful, of course, but that we don't have to take them so seriously. In other words: we don't have to believe them all.

Think a negative thought to yourself for fifteen seconds, and notice how it makes you feel. Make it real, a thought you would have in real life. It may be critical of yourself, or of somebody else. After the fifteen seconds, I want you to say the same thing again, but this time, I want you to say, 'I'm having the thought' before it.

Write down the difference you felt between the two phrases.

THE GIFT OF NOW

PRACTICING BEING PRESENT

We all hear about living in the present, being in the moment, or abiding in the here and now. But what does it mean, and how do we do it? These phrases are very easy to say, and in my view have become almost meaningless clichés. We cannot just will ourselves to live in the here and now. We find ourselves again and again living in the future.

Everything has a cause, and so does the fact that we seem unable to live in the present moment. So in order to do so, we need to look at what prevents us. It may or may not come as a surprise, but the reason for this is our attachment to thinking.

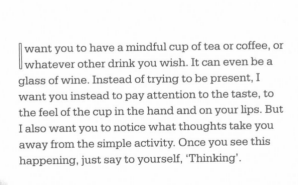

I want you to have a mindful cup of tea or coffee, or whatever other drink you wish. It can even be a glass of wine. Instead of trying to be present, I want you instead to pay attention to the taste, to the feel of the cup in the hand and on your lips. But I also want you to notice what thoughts take you away from the simple activity. Once you see this happening, just say to yourself, 'Thinking'.

How long did
you manage to
stay present?

What other activities
could you apply this
attention technique to?

PRACTICING BEING PRESENT

Chapter Eight
YOUR TRUE HOME

Most of us are fortunate enough to have a home, ideally a place where you can relax, be at ease and be yourself. My wife Gaynor and I have a very nice home which we love, and we share with our two lovely Border Collie dogs, Jaya and Bankei.

There are times when we need to leave, to go to work, go shopping, or on holiday. What I have noticed is that when we have been away for a while, on our return we look around the house, just to make sure everything is OK. We check that there have been no break-ins, that the roof isn't leaking, and so on. No matter how good a time we have had whilst being away, it is always nice to come back home.

We all have another home, which paradoxically you can never leave, but one which we rarely inhabit. Have you guessed what I am talking about? I am talking about your body. Your body is your home. Even if your body is not very healthy, it is still your home. If we never visited our house, what would happen to it? It would fall into disrepair through neglect. In the same way, we need to visit the home which is our body, to cherish it, to know when it needs attention, when it needs a walk, and so on. If we are not at home in the body, we cannot know its needs, or feel the intuition it contains.

BEING AT HOME

There is a well-known saying that goes, 'I have had many troubles in life, but most of them never happened.' I think this is so true of all of us: when we are not at home in the body we are lost in our thoughts and we create problems that have never existed

I suggest you put 20 minutes to one side for this, and do it twice a week.

1 Sit or lie quietly; feel your breath for a minute. Listen to any sounds, whether it's the traffic, the refrigerator, or the birds in your garden.

2 Now take your attention to your feet, and just feel the tingling energy in them. These feet work hard, even if they don't work very well. Can you show them a moment of appreciation?

3 Now move up and feel the rest of your legs: your knees, thighs and so on. Feel around your bodily home; feel the hips and appreciate just how much work they do every day.

4 Feel your hands; notice how sensitive they are.

Practice the meditation above for a few weeks and write down any changes that occur over time. Do you fall asleep more easily? Do you feel more relaxed or less anxious?

and never will exist. A home is a kind of refuge, and so is the body: when we are at home there, we are not in our own personal thought-made dramas about our lives. I am not saying things never need attending to, but if you pay attention you too will see that a lot of your problems are created in your head.

5 **Feel the sensations around your face, your mouth and cheeks. Take a moment to appreciate these and what they do for you.**

6 **Take your attention to your chest and your belly area; just experience how you feel here.**

7 **Just as a home has windows and doors which open to the world, so you have the senses. Take a moment to notice them: the sensations of your skin, your sight, your hearing, your tasting, and your sense of smell. This is how you encounter the world.**

Take a few moments just exploring these senses.

BODY GRATITUDE

It is so very easy to take our bodies for granted. There is actually very little we need to do to keep them in reasonable condition: a little good food, some exercise and rest, and that is about it. Even when we are sleeping, everything continues to work: the food is being digested, the heart is still beating, the organs are doing what they do without any input from ourselves. How wonderful that is!

Sit quietly and feel your breath for a few minutes. Now become aware of your whole body for a few moments then feel the different parts of the body: the feet, the hands, the hips; sense inside to the heart, the organs and so on.

When sensing each part just pause and give a little smile. Show your gratitude in this simple physical gesture, letting your body communicate to itself how much you appreciate yourself.

You can just sense these parts or you can imagine them in your mind's eye. It doesn't matter; do it in whichever way feels right.

After the exercise, write down your gratitude for your body.

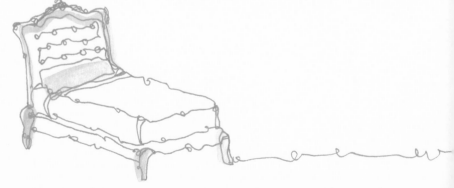

I am grateful for . . .

BODY GRATITUDE

EXAMINING MY BELIEFS AND ASSUMPTIONS

We all have views and beliefs about ourselves: our bodies, our lives, and indeed, just about everything else.

These are the assumptions and beliefs that we grow up with, but we rarely examine. One common definition of a belief is 'an acceptance that something exists or is true, especially one without proof'. So, to be free of these beliefs and assumptions, it is good to know what they are and how they developed.

Sit quietly, then, when you feel ready, fill in the blanks on the right.

I believe my body is . . .

because . . .

Other people believe me to be . . .

I believe I cannot do what I really want because . . .

I believe I will not get what I want in life because . . .

I believe . . .

I assume . . .

ACCEPTANCE

Acceptance is an important facet of the jewel of happiness. If we don't learn to accept things, we will remain in conflict.

For example, we may want people to like us, but we need to accept the reality that not everybody will. Sometimes people may even show their feelings of dislike towards us. If we were to strive against being disliked, we would be constantly disappointed and hurt. Acceptance enables us to look at life realistically and clearly, reducing our distress and increasing our happiness.

Acceptance is the opposite of denial: it moves us beyond helplessness into a position of power.

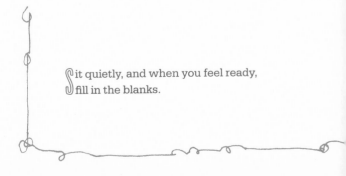

Sit quietly, and when you feel ready, fill in the blanks.

Acceptance, to me, means . . .

The one thing I cannot accept about the world is . . .

because . . .

The one thing I cannot accept about myself is . . .

because . . .

The one thing I cannot accept about other people is . . .

because . . .

If I could accept life on its terms I would be . . .

ACCEPTANCE

Chapter Nine

THE FORGOTTEN MEDICINE

When I was a young boy, my mom would take me to the doctor when I was unwell. I resisted this, because it seemed invariable that the medicine tasted awful. I remember having a bad cough once and she tried to give me a spoonful of the medicine, but, being a little drama queen, I would not open my mouth. However, I eventually relented, and it tasted foul.

As many of us have experienced, medicine doesn't always taste very nice – but ideally, it makes us well. There is another medicine available, a medicine for the mind, which also doesn't 'taste' pleasant but heals us.

This medicine is called mindfulness, or, to put it another way – doing nothing. Doing nothing is incredibly difficult for many of us, because we are addicted to doing, to being active. Many people have an inability to be still. Even when they are physically static, they are mentally active. Their mind swirls here, there and everywhere, never resting. It's not great for our health: we get tired and frazzled, we sleep badly, we suffer stress.

Doing nothing allows emotional processing to take place. It allows us to rest in just being here, rather than forever trying to get somewhere or achieve something. However, for many of us the medicine of doing nothing doesn't feel good, so we don't do it.

If we don't give the body and mind time to rest and to process the events of the day by sitting and doing nothing, then that processing will take place when we are at our most vulnerable: when we are sleeping. In the end, it's much more comfortable to work through it during the day.

THE FORGOTTEN MEDICINE

DO NOTHING AND NOTICE

Sitting and doing nothing can give us the opportunity to see just how caught up in the busy trap we are. We can begin to see how much we are propelled into doing by our restless energy and over-thinking mind. We all have a 'pusher self' inside which, if strongly developed, can easily keep us on the go all day and can lead to exhaustion.

Busy-ness is really laziness in disguise Think about this!

Sit and feel your body and its contact with the chair. Sense your breath rising and falling.

While doing this very simple thing, I want you to just notice when the urge to get busy and do something arises. It can be an urge to do anything, including to think about things.

When noticing and observing in this way always return back to the simple feeling of the breath, or the sounds in the distance.

How long did you manage to sit and do nothing? How did it make you feel? Track your progress with this exercise over the coming weeks.

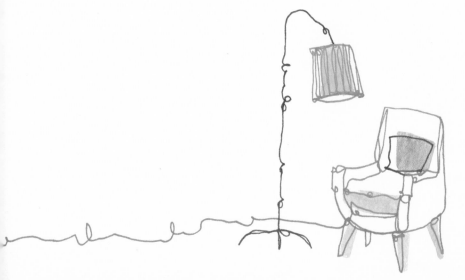

DO NOTHING AND NOTICE

MY AVOIDANCE STRATEGIES

We all yearn to live in the present moment, yet we are all masters at avoiding it. Some strategies we may fall into are things like keeping busy, drinking, overworking, being excessively ambitious, and focusing only on the future. Our phones and other devices can also be great distractions from facing ourselves. It is worth saying that there is nothing wrong with any of these activities; the problem is when we overdo them.

Over-thinking is also an avoidance mechanism it helps us to avoid our feelings. Some of us may close down emotionally and avoid people when things get difficult; others may go on the attack and blame others or themselves. There are many ways of avoidance, and too many to list here, but if you take a little time to be honest with yourself, the odds are that you'll know which are the ones you're most prone to.

Sit quietly and feel your breath for a few minutes. When you feel ready, ask yourself these questions and write down the responses.

What situations do I tend to avoid in my life?

 What situation or person did I avoid today?

 Why did I avoid this situation or person?

 How did I avoid them?

 What story did I tell myself and what feelings were present?

PAUSING

Many of us rush through life not noticing where we are and what we are doing. We can so easily get lost in a haze of activity. In the words of Albert Einstein,

'He . . . who can no longer pause to wonder and stand rapt in awe, is as good as dead; his eyes are closed.'

It seems to me that we have so many ideas, want to do so many things, aspire to so many goals, that we tread on the beauty and simplicity of this moment and what is has to offer.

We cannot appreciate and be grateful for what we have if we don't notice what we have. Bringing pauses back into your life can be a simple way of waking up to it.

Make the intention of bringing short pauses into your day. For example, can you refrain from doing something else when waiting for the kettle to boil? Can you take a few minutes to sit quietly without your phone and do nothing?

Just experience whichever senses are active; it may be hearing, watching the world go by, or closing your eyes and feeling the sensations in your skin and muscles.

Choose a day and make the intention of pausing several times. You don't need to do anything different, just suspend the thinking mind and feel what you are doing. Connect with your body, or whatever activity you are engaged in. Why don't you try it out now?

Gaze softly at this blank page for five minutes.

BREATHING SPACES

Over-thinking can be described as the art of creating problems that don't exist. Thinking itself, as we have previously mentioned, is a wonderful instrument we can learn to use wisely, but when we get too wrapped up in it, we can get stuck in a substitute life – one that only exists inside our heads.

We can learn to halt this habit by bringing breathing spaces into our lives. You can do this most days for just five to ten minutes.

Several times a day, take a breathing space. That means very simply come back to your breath. You can't be 'asleep', whether literally or figuratively, and simultaneously be aware of your breath. Just feel it several times a day for a few seconds, or a few minutes.

Sit quietly and comfortably on a chair or meditation cushion. Take one or two deep breaths; don't try to change their rhythm, just let them be what they are.

Feel your breath as it comes and goes. Pay a little more attention to the end of the out breath, as there is a natural letting go there. Really feel the end of the exhalation. Pay attention, too, to the start of the in breath, which is a new beginning. If you get involved in thoughts just silently repeat to yourself, 'Thinking'.

You are not trying to achieve anything here. Just feel the breath as it comes and goes, and when you are lost in thought, that's no problem; just label it as 'Thinking' and return your attention to your breathing.

Try it for a week and note down any feelings or changes.

117

THE OTHER MEDICINE:
HONESTY

Another good medicine for ourselves is that of honesty, and in particular, being truthful with ourselves. This is partly because we feel ashamed when we're deceitful or avoidant, and also because the fear of getting found out can leave us carrying a weight of resentment.

It is good to know how we view ourselves, but also to challenge those views. In the next exercise, don't think; write down your first gut answers.

Sit quietly and feel your breath for a few minutes, then fill in the blanks on the right.

I am very good at . . .

I am bad at . . .

One of my hidden talents is . . .

I would like to be really good at . . .

I am very . . . . in my relationships

My biggest regret is . . .

What I like about my body most is . . .

What I dislike about my body most is . . .

THE OTHER MEDICINE: HONESTY

WHAT I REALLY THINK OF MYSELF

We all have views about ourselves, which in some cases can be accurate, and in other cases are far from the mark. I always held the view that I could not do public speaking. I held this view for decades, until one day, at a Buddhist ceremony, I had to stand up and speak. I was terrified, but I did it. Since then, I've continued to speak in public, and eventually realized I have a natural talent for it. We can have many negative views of ourselves that can imprison us, but with just a little honesty and awareness we can begin to be free of them.

Fill in the blanks opposite and be as honest as you can. Don't think; just write.

Sit quietly and feel your breath for a few minutes then fill in the blanks

I am a . . . . person

My greatest gift is . . .

My worst habit is . . .

I will never learn to . . .

I really want to stop . . .

I get angry at . . .

I am happy when . . .

I know I can . . . . but I'm too scared to do it

WHAT I REALLY THINK OF MYSELF

WHAT OTHERS THINK OF ME

One of our biggest worries is the question of what other people think of us. There are many times where we hold back on doing something we know would benefit us and others, because we are scared about how some people may judge us. It's paralyzing, and can leave us feeling bitter and confused.

The truth is, though, that we project our own thoughts onto the outside world. The 'judgments' that hold us back aren't actually other people's, but our imagined versions of them. Those thoughts and judgments are your own.

me

Sit quietly for a few minutes and feel your breath, then fill in the blanks opposite.

My friends like me because . . .

My friends would say my worst quality is . . .

Some people don't like me because . . .

My boss thinks I am . . .

My children / partner would say I am . . .

In a crisis my friends would say I am . . .

My friends would say I am brilliant at . . .

My father would say I am . . .

My mother would say I am . . .

ME AND MY LIFE

Where is your life heading? You may have a vague idea, but we never know, and have limited control over, what may be around the corner.

You may also have views about yourself that you are not aware of, and those will definitely influence how your future unfolds. This is the one area of your life where you do have control – or at the very least, you can be honest about these views, and so weaken their hold on you.

Sit quietly for a few minutes and feel your breath, then fill in the blanks opposite.

My life is going . . . . right now

I have had a . . . . past

I have a . . . . future ahead of me

My biggest obstacle to a good future is . . .

My greatest asset to achieving a good future is . . .

I will have a good future because . . .

There will be obstacles in the future and I will meet them with . . .

My future is . . .

because . . .

ME AND MY LIFE

Chapter Ten

ARE YOU NEXTING?

I was once in a traffic jam when I glanced to my side and saw a woman walking along while texting on her phone. There is no judgment of the woman here, as most of us do this at times. I turned back for a few seconds, singing along to the radio, then turned and glanced again. I noticed that she was still texting, but I also noticed that she was leaning forward and rushing. Another word popped into my mind: nexting.

Each moment of our life is itself. We may be emptying the dishwasher, walking up the stairs, sending emails, or zipping up our jacket; these are the ordinary and everyday activities that make up our lives.

However, we tend to want to be in the next moment. This is what I mean by 'nexting.' We feel and believe that this moment as it is, is not enough. Emptying the dishwasher is not exciting, we believe; walking up the stairs is just about getting to some other place.

If we live in this way, what we end up doing is skimming across the surface. We live what we could call a horizontal life. This is not a satisfying way to live: what we want is depth. We yearn for a life of presence, but we have got into the habit of nexting, because somehow we believe that the next moment will be better, more exciting, or at least different.

The joy of life is not to be found in the next imagined moment, but in the very footsteps we take while walking up those stairs. Through mindfulness, we can learn to empty the dishwasher and be present whilst we are doing it.

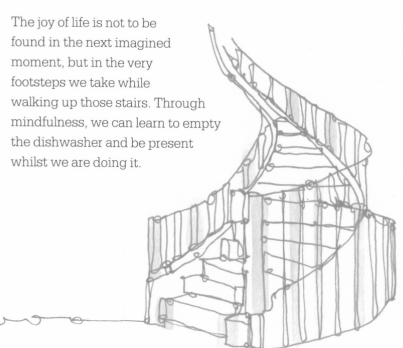

NOTICING YOUR NEXTING

We often feel that we lack something in our lives. We seem to believe that we can find that certain something, and that that something must be in the future; we just haven't found it yet. We don't quite know what it is, but we can exhaust ourselves trying to find it.

We also believe, falsely, that this sense of fulfilment cannot be found in our ordinary lives. What's so joyous, we might ask, about sitting in traffic?

This very belief is the source of our nexting into the next moment, and takes us away from the innate joy that is within life itself. But it's waiting to be discovered, if we can learn to be present while we are living it.

Sit and be quiet for ten minutes, feel your breath rising and falling. At some point you will drift off into nexting about the future, or remembering the past. Once you notice this, I want you to quickly write down, in brief, what thoughts took you away. In other words: the theme. Was it planning? Was it an anxious thought? Was it a fantasy about a holiday? Best to keep it simple. For example, if it was anxiety, just write down 'anxious thought'. Remember this is not a judgment, only an observation.

My distracting thoughts:

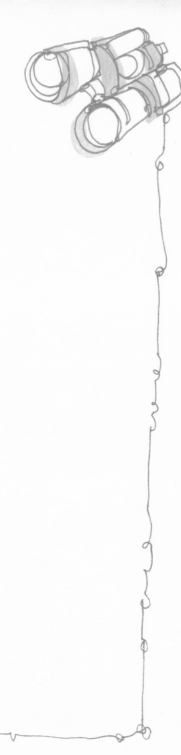

NOTICE YOUR NEXTING

WHAT AM I LOOKING FOR?

As I say, we are all looking for something, but we are not quite sure what. We may assume it's a perfect job, a perfect partner, or to live in the perfect climate; we may believe it is being approved of, or being famous.

In this exercise, be open to anything that arises, then write it down. It doesn't matter how ridiculous or silly it may seem. Don't censor yourself, but welcome whatever comes. You might see sides to yourself you didn't realize you had, and having greeted them, can release their energy.

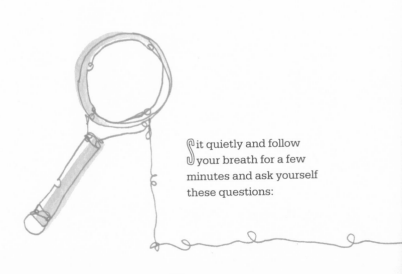

Sit quietly and follow your breath for a few minutes and ask yourself these questions:

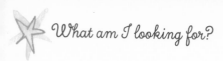 What am I looking for?

 What am I really looking for?

 What is the one thing I am looking for?

WHAT AM I RESISTING IN THIS MOMENT?

All human beings resist being in the present moment: we'd rather be thinking about our lives in general than experiencing them in this exact second. In the ancient Buddhist tradition, this is called Upādāna. Upādāna is that tendency to attach to our stories and our own thought-made dramas, and it can create a lot of distress, because they are often anxiety-based. To be happy, we need to identify these stories and to let them go. We don't need to create new stories, but to relax our tendency to get lost in the ones we already have.

Sit quietly for a few minutes and feel your breath then ask yourself this question. What am I resisting in this moment? Write down everything, do your best not to censor yourself.

After a few minutes, ask yourself the remaining questions opposite. Write everything down. Wait a few minutes then carry on with your day.

What am I resisting in this moment?

 What am I really resisting?

 What is the one thing I am resisting?

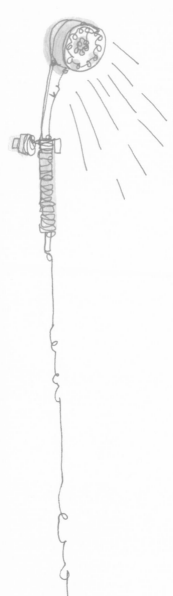

WHEN AM I NEXTING?

Spend a few minutes choosing three activities that you are going to be mindful of during your day. You can write them down to remind you.

The activities could be brushing your teeth, walking up or down the stairs or taking a shower. You can pick these or choose your own; they don't have to be anything spectacular.

I want you to notice when you are nexting during these activities – in other words when you begin to rush or get lost in thinking about something else. For example, you may be having a shower and realize that you are mentally arguing with your boss. At that point, say to yourself 'Thinking,' and return back to the feeling of having a shower.

Afterwards, make notes of the distractions you experienced during your three chosen activities. Just keep them brief.

1

I was . . .

when I started . . .

2

I was . . .

when I started . . .

3

I was . . .

when I started . . .

MASKS I WANT PEOPLE TO SEE

One reason why we spend our lives nexting is that we don't feel authentic, and that can make us feel uncomfortable. To feel more comfortable, we wear masks or present parts of ourselves we believe other people want to see.

We looked at identifying masks in chapter one. In this exercise we are going to explore the masks we use a little further.

Sit quietly for a few minutes and feel the breath. Write down the masks you want people to see. Then fill in the blanks.

My most treasured mask is . . .

I treasure this mask because . . .

Without this mask I would . . .

Without this mask people will . . .

My most important mask at work is . . .

This is because it . . .

Without this mask I would . . .

People like this mask because . . .

The mask I want people to see most is . . .

This is because it . . .

PARTS I DON'T WANT PEOPLE TO SEE

As well as presenting to the world a series of masks that we are comfortable with or want people to see, we also have parts of ourselves that we want to keep hidden. We don't want people to see them because they either don't fit into our preferred self-image, or we fear we will be rejected for them. This is quite exhausting: banishing habits or behaviors means our mind has to stay busy keeping them out. That's one sure way to end up nexting, as we are trying to run away from ourselves.

In this exercise we are exploring the parts we don't want others, or ourselves, to see.

Sit quietly for a few minutes and feel the breath. Write down the parts you don't want people to see, then fill in the remaining blanks opposite.

Parts I don't want people to see . . .

The part of me I definitely don't want people to see is . . .

If I let this part out it would . . .

What is positive about this part of me is . . .

If people saw this part they would . . .

The part I don't want to see in myself is . . .

If I allowed all my hidden parts to be seen it would . . .

REVISITING YOUR INTUITIVE SELF

Before we end, I want you to revisit your
intuitive self. If your life is out of balance,
it can be one of your best sources of insight.
Set aside your usual modus operandi, and
tune in to deeper-felt senses about your life.

§it quietly and feel your breath for
a few minutes. Then, when you
feel ready, answer these questions,
using your non-dominant hand:

*Hello intuitive self;
how are you right now?*

We have spoken more recently; how has that been?

 How am I doing from your point of view?

 Do you have anything to say about how to go forward into my future?

 Anything else?

HAPPINESS FOR SELF AND WORLD

Remember, none of us live in a vacuum.
We are social beings, and to be truly happy
is to want happiness for other people too.

I want to finish by introducing you to a short
happiness-for-all meditation.

1 Start by sitting quietly and feeling your breath.

2 Then take your attention to your heart area – the center of your chest. Just sense this area and feel what's there, even if nothing much seems to be happening.

3 Now, simply drop this phrase into the area: may I be well, may I be happy.

5 Gradually welcome a good friend into your heart. Repeat the phrase: may you be well, may you be happy.

6 After a minute or two, welcome work colleagues, or those whom you may not naturally want to invite into your heart. Repeat the phrase: may you all be well, may you all be happy.

7 Finish with a sense of the whole world and welcome it into your heart. Repeat the phrase: may every living being be happy and free from pain.

7 Sit back again and feel your heart. You are planting seeds of happiness here.

8 Relax.

HAPPINESS FOR SELF AND WORLD

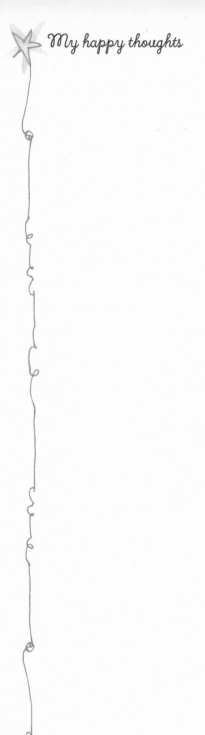

My happy thoughts